CW01044036

THE OFFICIAL SHREWSBURY TOWN QUIZ BOOK

THE OFFICIAL SHREWSBURY TOWN QUIZ BOOK

Compiled by Chris Cowlin
and David Williams

Foreword by Mickey Brown

Best wishes
Chris Cowlin

APEX PUBLISHING LTD

Hardback first published in 2009 by
Apex Publishing Ltd
PO Box 7086, Clacton on Sea, Essex, CO15 5WN, England
www.apexpublishing.co.uk

British Library Cataloguing-in-Publication Data
A catalogue record for this book
is available from the British Library

ISBN HARDBACK: 1-906358-24-9 978-1-906358-24-2

Typeset in 10.5pt Chianti Bdlt Win95BT

Cover Design: Siobhan Smith

Printed in Great Britain by the MPG Books Group,
Bodmin and King's Lynn

Author's Note:
Please can you contact me: **ChrisCowlin@btconnect.com** *if you find any mistakes/errors in this book as I would like to put them right on any future reprints of this book. I would also like to hear from Shrewsbury Town fans who have enjoyed the test! For more information on me and my books please look at:* **www.ChrisCowlin.com**

This book is an official product of Shrewsbury Town Football Club

We would like to dedicate this book to:

All the players and staff who have worked for the club during their history.

FOREWORD

I am honoured to have been asked to write the foreword to 'The Official Shrewsbury Town Quiz Book' compiled by Chris Cowlin and David Williams.

I had three spells at the club; I first arrived in the 1980s as an apprentice and break into the first team the year later. I played with some great players during my time at the club and played under various managers. I made a club record 418 League appearances, scoring 36 goals. It was a great moment in my career when the club were crowned Division Three Champions in 1993/1994 and when I helped to keep the club in the Football League by scoring against Exeter City in the 2-1 away win in May 2000. I played my last game for The Shrews in 2001 and joined Boston United, I can honesty say that I have had an enjoyable football career which has lasted over 20 years. I would advise you to remember these facts as they will help when you are answering the Mickey Brown section!

The history of Shrewsbury Town is long and varied and I'm sure the questions included in this book will bring back plenty of memories.

Having been fortunate enough to see a preview of this book, I know that Shrewsbury Town fans of all ages will be entertained for hours with questions about the Shrews past

and present.

As the club continues to write new chapters in its history, it is always fitting to remember what went before.

I hope you all enjoy this wonderful quiz book as much as I did.

Mickey Brown

Best wishes
Mickey Brown

INTRODUCTION

I would first of all like to thank Mickey Brown for writing the foreword to this book. I am very grateful for his help on this project.

I would also like to thank the Shropshire Star, Beacon Radio and BBC Shropshire for their comments and reviews on this book (these can be found at the back of the book).

I would also like to thank Ian Whitfield at Shrewsbury Town Football Club for his help during the books compilation.

I hope you enjoy this book. Hopefully it should bring back some wonderful memories!

It was great to work with David Williams for the first time, between us I hope we have given you a selection of easy, medium and hard questions.

In closing, I would like to thank all my friends and family for encouraging me to complete this book.

Best wishes
Chris Cowlin

Visit Chris Cowlin's website:

www.ChrisCowlin.com

Visit David Williams' website:

www.desertengland.com

HISTORY OF THE CLUB

1. *Can you name the club's two nicknames?*

2. *In which year was the club formed – 1884, 1885 or 1886?*

3. *Which League did Shrewsbury Town win in the 1949/1950 season and then get admitted into Division Three North at the start of the1950/1951 season?*

4. *Who became the club's first player-manager in 1958?*

5. *Which competition were Shrewsbury Town playing in during their first Wembley appearance in 1996?*

6. *The club changed their colours from blue and white to what in 1978 to 1982?*

7. *Which player holds the record for appearing the most times for Shrewsbury Town in his three spells at the club?*

8. *In which year were the club League Cup semi-finalists?*

9. *Which manager won the Third Division Championship during 1978/1979, which was his first season in charge at the club?*

10. *By what score line did Shrewsbury beat Swindon Town in May 1955 in Division Three South, this result remains the club's biggest ever League win in their history – 5-0, 6-0 or 7-0?*

NATIONALITIES – 1

Match the player to his nationality

11.	Guy Madjo	Northern Irish
12.	Ben Davies	Australian
13.	Darren Moss	English
14.	Shane Cansdell-Sherriff	Welsh
15.	James Meredith	English
16.	Derek Asamoah	English
17.	Jimmy Quinn	Ghanaian
18.	Paul Evans	Cameroonian
19.	Graham Turner	Welsh
20.	Wayne Clarke	Australian

1990s

21. Who managed the club between 1993 and 1997?

22. How many of the club's 46 League matches did they win during 1995/1996?

23. Which striker was the club's top League scorer during 1996/1997 with 17 goals in 41 matches?

24. Can you name the three players who scored double figures for The Shrews in the 1997/1998 League season?

25. Which midfielder signed for Town in September 1991 from Sheffield Wednesday and later left for Hereford United in 1998?

26. Who managed the club between January 1990 and January 1991?

27. How many points did Shrewsbury Town finish with during 1992/1993 having finished ninth in the League – 60 points, 62 points or 64 points?

28. Which midfielder signed for Plymouth Argyle when he left Town in March 1998 having signed from West Ham United to join Shrewsbury in 1996?

29. Which Scottish striker scored 10 League goals during 1998/1999 in his 32 starts and five substitute appearances?

30. How many of the club's 46 League matches did they draw during 1998/1999?

SQUAD NUMBERS – 2008/2009 – 1

Match up the player with his Shrewsbury Town squad number

31.	Ben Davies	2
32.	Marc Pugh	12
33.	Kelvin Langmead	19
34.	Neil Ashton	20
35.	Guy Madjo	14
36.	Ben Herd	3
37.	Steven Hindmarch	9
38.	Dave Hibbert	11
39.	Michael Symes	8
40.	Darren Moss	7

WHERE DID THEY COME FROM – 1

Match the player to the club they joined Shrewsbury Town from

41.	Russell Crossley	Newcastle United
42.	Alan Durban	Aston Villa
43.	Grant Holt	Rotherham United
44.	Shane Cansdell-Sherriff	Celtic
45.	Howard Clark	Bristol City
46.	Graham Clapham	Derby County
47.	Graham Coughlan	Liverpool
48.	John Keay	Tranmere Rovers
49.	Paul Wimbleton	Nottingham Forest
50.	Barry Stobart	Coventry City

MANAGERS

Match the manager to the period of time he was in charge at Shrewsbury Town

51.	Alan Durban	1993-1997
52.	John Bond	1984-1987
53.	Jimmy Quinn	1999-2003
54.	Gary Peters	1974-1978
55.	Kevin Ratcliffe	1991-1993
56.	Harry Gregg	1950-1954
57.	Chic Bates	1997-1999
58.	Jake King	2003-2004
59.	Sammy Crooks	1968-1972
60.	Fred Davies	2004-2008

INTERNATIONALS

Match the player to the number of caps for his country

61.	Sandy Brown	5 Scotland Under-21 Caps
62.	Mark Williams	5 England Under-19 Caps
63.	Nigel Jemson	36 Northern Ireland Caps
64.	Mickey Thomas	1 England Under-21 Cap
65.	Scott Howie	1 Scotland Cap
66.	Doug Rougvie	48 Northern Ireland Caps
67.	John McGinlay	51 Wales Caps
68.	Jimmy Quinn	13 Scotland Caps
69.	Paul Evans	1 Scotland Cap
70.	Joe Hart	2 Wales Caps

LEAGUE APPEARANCES – 1

Match the player to the number of League appearances he made for Shrewsbury Town

71.	**George Boardman**	*91 (5)*
72.	**Wayne Williams**	*274 (20)*
73.	**Peter Wall**	*100 (1)*
74.	**Chic Bates**	*176 (18)*
75.	**Anthony Kelly**	*85*
76.	**Neil Lyne**	*172 (4)*
77.	**Alan Finley**	*77 (3)*
78.	**David Moyes**	*212 (9)*
79.	**Harry Middleton**	*18*
80.	**Colin Robinson**	*60 (3)*

THE LEAGUE CUP

81. *Which England international signed for Blackburn Rovers the day Town travelled there for 1993's tie?*

82. *Who scored his first goal for Fulham and the game's only goal to knock Town out of the 2007/2008 League Cup in the second round?*

83. *Town made a dramatic debut in the League Cup by reaching which stage in 1961?*

84. *Which player scored in all four games of the 1991/92 Cup run?*

85. *In 1986/87, a late goal from Bernard McNally ensured a quarter-final place at the expense of which club whose fans rioted after the match?*

86. *During Town's dramatic Division Three title year in 1978/79, which round did they get knocked out of in the League Cup?*

87. *How many times did Town crash out in the first round during the 1970s?*

88. *How many League Cup goals did Arthur Rowley score in his Shrewsbury career?*

89. *After reaching the semi-final in 1961, when was the next time Town got beyond the third round?*

90. *Who knocked Town out of the 2008/09 Carling Cup first round by winning 1-0?*

GOALKEEPERS

91. ***Steve Perks signed professional terms with Shrewsbury in which year – 1980, 1981 or 1982?***

92. ***Which goalkeeper arrived after spending the previous season as understudy to Bruce Grobbelaar at Liverpool in 1982?***

93. ***Which goalkeeper was named in the Shrewsbury squad 10 weeks before his 16th birthday on 1 February 2003?***

94. ***What was the name of the Town goalkeeper famed for taking penalties around the time of the First World War?***

95. ***Which Town goalkeeper and county javelin champion tragically died in the open swimming pool at Trentham Gardens in 1963?***

96. ***The father of a recent England goalkeeper started in the sticks for Town in the 1965/66 season, who was he?***

97. ***Which goalkeeper saved three successive penalties to ensure a Conference play-off win on spot-kicks over Aldershot in 2004?***

98. ***Which goalkeeper's record run of 236 League games was brought to an end by injury in December 1977?***

99. ***Who was Steve Ogrizovic's understudy from 1982-84 and later made the No 1 jersey his own?***

100. ***Steve Perks and Ken Hughes's domination of the goal keeper's jersey was finally ended by which stopper in 1991?***

POSITIONS IN THE LEAGUE – 1

Match the position Shrewsbury Town finished to the season

101.	2007/2008	3rd
102.	2006/2007	22nd
103.	2005/2006	24th
104.	2004/2005	15th
105.	2003/2004	10th
106.	2002/2003	7th
107.	2001/1002	18th
108.	2000/2001	21st
109.	1999/2000	15th
110.	1998/1999	9th

ATTENDANCES

111. In which season did Town suffer a loss of £151, 575 despite an average first season attendance in Division Two of 7,782?

112. 18,000 watched Shrewsbury entertain which high-flying side in 1980/81's FA Cup, drawing 0-0 before losing the replay?

113. Shrewsbury's biggest gate for some time came in the fifth round of the FA Cup against Arsenal in 1989 when how many turned up – 11,356, 12,356 or 13,356?

114. Town's first ever Shropshire League game in 1890 against Wellington attracted how many fans – 40, 400 or 4,000?

115. A then record 14,500 fans turned up to the Gay Meadow to watch Town draw 2-2 in which Cup final in 1938?

116. How much did it cost to watch Town from the Riverside during their first season in the League in 1950?

117. Town's first home victory as a League club over Wrexham in 1950 attracted how many fans 'officially' – 14,070, 15,070 or 16,070?

118. According to media reports, how many Town fans travelled to watch their fifth round exit at the hands of Chelsea in 1965/66 – 5,000, 10,000 or 15,000?

119. Why was the Gay Meadow's capacity reduced from 16,000 to 8,000 in 1989?

120. Against who was Town's biggest ever attendance of 18,917 recorded against in 1961?

BIG WINS – 1

Match up the game to the final score

121.	v. Southport (home), May 1968, League	6-0
122.	v. Port Vale (home), September 1970, League	9-0
123.	v. Blackburn Rovers (home), October 1971, League	5-2
124.	v. Colchester United (away), November 1971, FA Cup 1st round	7-4
125.	v. Welshpool (home), December 1973, Welsh Cup	7-3
126.	v. Llanidloes (home), December 1974, Welsh Cup	5-1
127.	v. Doncaster Rovers (home), February 1975, League	4-1
128.	v. Bury (home), April 1978, League	7-1
129.	v. Rhyl (home), January 1979, Welsh Cup	5-0
130.	v. Fulham (home), May 1980, League	5-3

1999/2000

131. ***Which manager was in charge at the start of the season and left in November 2008?***

132. ***Following on from the previous question, which former Chester City manager took charge of The Shrews in November 2008, and was Shrewsbury Town manager until April 2003?***

133. ***True or false: It took Shrewsbury Town six attempts to win their first League game of season?***

134. ***Against which team did Shrewsbury beat 4-1 at home during September 1999, despite being 1-0 down after 45 minutes?***

135. ***Which Essex based team did Shrewsbury beat 2-1 at home during April 2000 with Lee Steele scoring both goals, both being penalties?***

136. ***What was the score when Shrewsbury played Hull City at home during November 1999 – 3-0 to Shrewsbury Town, a 1-1 draw or 3-0 to Hull City?***

137. ***Who finished the club's highest scorer with 11 League goals in his 34 starts and three substitute appearances?***

138. ***Which team did Shrewsbury Town beat 2-1 away on the last day of the League season?***

139. ***How many of the club's 46 League matches did they win – 9, 15 or 21?***

140. ***How many of the club's 46 League matches did they draw – 13, 15 or 17?***

WHO AM I? – 1

141. I am a goalkeeper and signed for The Shrews in 2007 on a free transfer from Leyton Orient.

142. I managed the club between October 1972 and December 1973.

143. I was born in Birmingham in 1957 and made 273 League starts and six substitute appearances for Town, scoring 58 League goals. I left for Sunderland in August 1982.

144. I am a forward and wore the number 8 shirt during 2008/2009.

145. I played in goal for The Shrews between 1982 and 1984 and made 84 League appearances for the club, when I left the club I signed for Coventry City.

146. I was born in Malta and scored 17 League goals in 41 matches during 1996/1997, I played for The Shrews between 1994 and 1997 and then again between 2002 and 2003.

147. I was born in Birmingham in 1981 and play in midfield, my previous clubs include Chester, Kidderminster and Walsall.

148. I am Welsh, born in 1974 and played for Shrewsbury Town between 1993 and 1999, when I left the club I went to play for Brentford.

149. I am a Scottish forward and played for The Shrews between January 1998 and March 2000, I scored 15 League goals.

150. I managed the club between December 1974 and February 1978.

LEAGUE GOALSCORERS – 1

Match the player with the number of League goals he scored for Shrewsbury Town

151.	Gary Hackett	59
152.	George Andrews	5
153.	Sagi Burton	17
154.	Frank Clarke	64
155.	Derek Asamoah	49
156.	Paul Petts	58
157.	Colin Murdock	10
158.	Colin Whitaker	2
159.	Ian Atkins	16
160.	Chic Bates	77

THE FA CUP

161. *Who scored the only goal – and his last for Town in a 1-0 home win against Wimbledon to set up the famous fifth round match with Arsenal in 1991?*

162. *Following on from the previous question, who netted the only goal for Arsenal in the 1-0 home defeat in the fifth round?*

163. *Against which club did Shrewsbury score three goals against three different goalkeepers in 1980?*

164. *In which year did Town first qualify for the opening round of the FA Cup after five preliminary rounds?*

165. *What was so unusual about Town's FA Cup tie with Dudley in 1935?*

166. *When Town recorded their first FA Cup victory for eight years in 1953, what was the significance of their next round match against Southampton?*

167. *Town's first venture into the last 16 ended with defeat in 1965 to which team that was top of Division One?*

168. *Town recorded a thumping win over Marine in the first round in 1996. What was the final score – 7-2, 9-2 or 11-2?*

169. *After upsetting Fulham in round three in 1996, which top-flight team did The Shrews beat in the fourth round?*

170. *Which club ended Shrewsbury's greatest FA Cup run at the quarter-final stage in 1982?*

MATCH THE YEAR – 1

Match up the year to the event

171.	Stephen Jagielka made his Shrews League debut	1976
172.	David Hunt was born	2003
173.	Luke Rodgers left Shrewsbury Town and joined Crewe Alexandra	1991
174.	John Bond took over as manager of Shrewsbury Town	2008
175.	Carl Griffiths finished top goal scorer in Division Three	1982
176.	Chris Humphrey made his Shrews League debut	1982
177.	Paul Simpson took over as manager of The Shrews	2005
178.	Nigel Jemson played his last game for Shrewsbury Town	1997
179.	Hereford United beat The Shrews 6-5 in the Welsh Cup semi-final replay	1993
180.	Shane Cansdell-Sherriff was born	2006

1980s

181. ***Despite reaching the quarter-final of the FA Cup, club legends Jake King (304 games) and Carlton Leonard (224) were released at the end of which season?***

182. ***After losing 5-0 to Hereford United in a Welsh Cup replay, Shrewsbury finished which season with a 10-match unbeaten spell in Division Two?***

183. ***Nicknamed Bomber, which full back signed professionally on his 18th birthday in November 1981 and became a fixture for the best part of the decade?***

184. ***Who did Town draw 0-0 with on the final game of the 1981/82 season to ensure Division Two survival?***

185. ***After 47 years of covering Shrewsbury, which journalist considered as 'obligatory reading' by fans, retired in 1982?***

186. ***The stunning goal by which player in 1983/84 graced the opening credits of Match of the Day for the rest of the season?***

187. ***Why couldn't Shrewsbury go on their usual pre-season tour of Scotland in 1985?***

188. ***Which player was signed in 1985/86 as Chic Bates' first 'big' name?***

189. ***Which player suffered an agonising snapped Achilles injury during his 400th League game against Ipswich Town in 1986?***

190. ***For three glorious seasons from 1982, what was Town's lowest finish in the old Division Two?***

2000/2001

191. In which position did the club finish in the League – 5th, 10th or 15th?

192. Against which team did Shrewsbury record their first League win of the season, in their fifth League match of the season during September 2000 away from home, with Nigel Jemson scoring twice and Mickey Brown the other goal?

193. Which team did Shrewsbury Town beat 7-1 away from home during February 2001?

194. Following on from the previous question, who scored a hat-trick in the game?

195. Which striker scored a brace in the 3-0 home win on the final day of the season during May 2001 against Brighton & Hove Albion?

196. Which defender signed from Notts County, initially on loan in November 2000 and then permanently during January 2001?

197. How many of the club's 46 League matches did they win?

198. Which striker finished the club's highest League scorer with 15 goals in 41 starts?

199. Who managed The Shrews during this season?

200. Which defender did Shrewsbury Town sell to Cardiff City during February 2001 for £450,000?

DEAN SPINK

201. Dean made a name for himself as a centre back for The Shrews but was originally signed for what position?

202. Which Shrews manager allegedly said: "You will never make it as a forward."?

203. From which club did Shrewsbury sign Dean in 1990?

204. How many years was Dean a part of the Shrewsbury squad?

205. In which position did Dean return to the club after his playing days were over?

206. After more than 300 League games for The Shrews, which club did Dean move on to?

207. Dean has tried his hand at management only once in a 'joint' role at which club?

208. In 2004, Dean won 68% of the votes in a BBC online poll to be named the club's what?

209. Which Welsh club did Dean sign for in the latter days of his playing career?

210. In 1999, Dean returned to Shrewsbury on loan to play in how many matches – four, five or six?

NATIONALTIES – 2

Match up the player with his nationality

211.	Sandy Brown	English
212.	Nigel Pearson	Northern Irish
213.	Graham Coughlan	Welsh
214.	John McGinlay	Northern Irish
215.	Bernard McNally	Welsh
216.	Carl Griffiths	English
217.	Ross MacLaren	Irish
218.	Mark Williams	Scottish
219.	Mickey Thomas	Scottish
220.	Ian Woan	Scottish

STEVE ANTHROBUS

221. ***With which London team did Steve launch his professional career?***

222. ***How much did Wimbledon part with to obtain Steve's services in 1989?***

223. ***How many League goals did Steve score during his six years with the Crazy Gang?***

224. ***When Shrewsbury played Liverpool in the FA Cup 4th round in 1996, which former Millwall team mate marked him as a Reds defender?***

225. ***How many League goals did Steve score for Shrewsbury in his career?***

226. ***To which club did Steve move to from Shrewsbury in 1997?***

227. ***Which successful League of Wales side did Steve figure in during the 2002 season?***

228. ***Steve went on to taste success with which non-League side that won the FA Trophy at Villa Park in 2004?***

229. ***Following on from the previous question, during that final, cup-tied team mate Chris Gray volunteered to carry out which duty for the final?***

230. ***Steve has managed only one at which non-League Midlands club?***

SHIRT SPONSORS

Match up the company with the years they sponsored Shrewsbury Town

231.	1982-86	Greenhous
232.	1987-88	Greenhous
233.	1988-89	Ternhill Communications
234.	1990-92	Morris Lubricants
235.	1992-95	Davenports
236.	1995-97	Link 51
237.	1997-99	WSJ
238.	1999-05	Wem Ales
239.	2005-07	Greenhous
240.	2007-08	RMW

AUSTIN BERKLEY

241. Austin was signed for The Shrews in 1995 from which club?

242. How much did Shrewsbury pay for Austin when he joined the club?

243. One of Austin's best moments came when his outstanding run and cross set up a 1996 FA Cup third round winning goal for which player against Fulham?

244. Where did Austin finish in the BBC's 'all-time Shrewsbury Town cult hero' poll in 2004?

245. How many League appearances did Austin make for The Shrews before leaving?

246. Following on from the previous question, to which club did Austin move from Shrewsbury in 2000?

247. While Austin was known for his silky skills on the field, which musical instrument did he enjoy playing when he was off of it?

248. Which pop star do Town fans claim Austin has a striking resemblance to?

249. How many League goals did Austin score for Town in his career – 22, 32 or 42?

250. At which club did Austin begin his career?

PAUL SIMPSON

251. How many times was Paul capped for England U21s?

252. After starting his career with Manchester City, which club did Paul join for £200,000 in 1988?

253. Paul was captain of which team that gained promotion to the old First Division in 1996?

254. In 1997, Paul's Wolves team lost to the eventual winners in the semi final of the FA Cup. Who were they?

255. With six goals in nine games, which club did Paul help into the old third division play-offs in 2002?

256. Which club did Paul take back into the Football League in 2005 as manager, and then up to the Football League One in successive seasons?

257. Who did Paul replace as manager at Preston North End in June 2006?

258. Who did Paul surprisingly point the finger at for Preston's bad run of results early in the 2007/08 season?

259. Which manager did Paul replace at Shrewsbury Town in March 2008?

260. Which year was he named League Two Manager of the Year and finished top of the League Managers Association statistics for the country as a whole?

WHERE DID THEY GO – 1

Match up the player with the team they joined after leaving Shrewsbury Town

261.	Alan Boswell	Swansea
262.	Paul Tester	Sunderland
263.	Derek Price	Aston Villa
264.	Paul Maguire	Hereford United
265.	David Poutney	Hereford United
266.	Carl Leonard	Stoke City
267.	Albert Harley	Bournemouth
268.	Howard Clark	Aldershot
269.	Ian Atkins	Wolves
270.	John Arnott	Hereford United

ARTHUR ROWLEY

271. *Arthur holds the current title as Football League's what?*

272. *How many goals did Arthur score during his entire playing career?*

273. *In which year did Arthur make his Shrewsbury Town debut?*

274. *And what period was he manager of Shrewsbury Town?*

275. *With which club did Arthur first turn professional in 1944?*

276. *With Leicester in 1956/57, Arthur scored a staggering 44 goals in how many League games?*

277. *How much did Shrewsbury pay for Arthur to become player-manager in 1958?*

278. *His 38 League goals during his first season in charge ensured Shrewsbury were promoted from which League?*

279. *Whose all-time League goal scoring record did he break?*

280. *Who did Arthur score his record-breaking 380th League goal against in 1961 whilst playing for Town?*

AUTO WINDSCREENS SHIELD RUNNERS-UP – 1996

281. Who did Town lose to in the final?

282. Which future Town player bagged both goals for the visitors?

283. Which Welsh international started for Town during his loan spell from Wolves?

284. Who was The Shrews manager during the road to Wembley?

285. In which minute did Shrewsbury Town pull a goal back - 60th, 70th or 80th?

286. Who scored Town's goal in the final?

287. Who did Shrewsbury beat in the south area final to reach Wembley?

288. Who was Town's Wembley final captain?

289. Who was in goal for Town in the final?

290. In which League position did Town finish during this season, the old Division Two?

NIGEL PEARSON

291. Nigel joined Shrewsbury Town in 1981 from which non-League club?

292. How old was Nigel when he made his Shrewsbury debut against Oldham in the old second division?

293. Against which Yorkshire club did Nigel score the first of five goals for Shrewsbury during March 1983 in a League match at Gay Meadow that Town won 3-1?

294. In which season was Nigel ever present for The Shrews, playing in all 42 League games?

295. Which club paid £250,000 to take him away from Shrewsbury after six years in 1987?

296. Can you name the third and final League club Nigel played for in his career?

297. Following on from the previous question, who was the manager that signed him in 1994 for £750,000?

298. Which club did Nigel begin his managerial career with?

299. Nigel has been caretaker manager of Newcastle United twice, the second time when Sam Allardyce was sacked, but who did he step in for in 2006?

300. Although never managing the full team, which management role has Pearson held with England?

WHERE DID THEY COME FROM – 2

Match the player to the club they joined Shrewsbury Town from

301.	Graeme Worsley	Carlisle United
302.	Gary Patterson	West Bromwich Albion
303.	Alex McGregor	West Ham United
304.	Guy Madjo	Macclesfield Town
305.	Michael Jackson	Bury
306.	Gary Leonard	Hibernian
307.	Paul Gorman	Bootle
308.	Kevin McIntyre	Blackpool
309.	John Arnott	Notts County
310.	John Halpin	Cheltenham Town

2001/2002

311. Which veteran defender who played 44 League games for Town from 1990/1991, scoring six goals, rejoined to boost the promotion push after a successful spell with Plymouth Argyle?

312. In which position in the League did The Shrews finish?

313. Which team finished below Shrewsbury but was playing in the Premier League in the 2008/09 season?

314. Currently known as the Coca-Cola League Two, but what was the division known as during this season?

315. Which player hit the limelight with a hat-trick over Rochdale in a 7-1 away win but was sent off for receiving his second yellow card for the goal celebration?

316. Which former Nottingham Forest star did Town sign in January 2002 from American club Miami Fusion?

317. Who was the teenage midfielder that had already been with the club for two seasons and made 19 League appearances during this season?

318. Which club won the League with a record 102 points during this season?

319. Who was the Town manager during this season?

320. Which player scored Town's goals in the two 1-0 away wins from the opening three games of the season?

IAN ATKINS

321. In what year did Ian turn professional with Shrewsbury Town, making his first appearance against Walsall in a 2-0 away defeat?

322. How many goals did the defender/midfielder score from his 279 League appearances, six as a substitute?

323. Which team did Ian move to for £80,000 in 1982?

324. Following on from the previous question, which player moved the other way as part of the deal?

325. Ian was a squad player in which Division One winning team in the 1984/85 season?

326. Ian's first coaching role came with Colchester United in 1990, but into which League had they just been relegated?

327. At which club did Ian end his playing days at in the old Third Division in 1993/94?

328. In 2000, Ian was at the helm of which club that lost its football league status after 69 years, following Town's great escape?

329. Four consecutive wins and a draw on the last day of the season in May 2006 saw Ian guide which side to League survival?

330. During Ian's playing career, what was the highest fee paid for his services by a club - £100,000, £500,000 or £1 million?

BERNARD McNALLY

331. Bernard was a part of the Northern Ireland squad at which World Cup finals?

332. Following on from the previous question, how many caps did Bernard win for his country during his career?

333. Although he represented Northern Ireland, where was Bernard born?

334. As a holding midfielder, goals were scarce, but how many League goals did he manage for The Shrews from almost 300 appearances?

335. Which club did Bernard join after leaving the Gay Meadow?

336. Following on from the previous question, the transfer fee was decided by a tribunal in July 1989 which eventually settled on how much to be paid?

337. Bernard helped one non-League club to the fourth round of the FA Cup, eventually losing to Middlesbrough 3-2 during 1996/97, but who were they?

338. Bernard was appointed the first manager of which club in 2004 that was reformed by fans after recently going bust?

339. As a West Brom player, which division did Bernard taste both relegation from and promotion to?

340. Bernard picked up his first overseas appointment in 2008 by becoming head coach to a club playing in which country?

2008/2009

341. Which player was named League Two Player of the Month for November 2008?

342. Who did Town beat 7-0 in the Football League Trophy match in October 2008?

343. Town started the League season with a 4-0 victory over whom?

344. The unbeaten League start ended in the fifth match when who beat Town 1-0 away?

345. Who was the only player to score more than one in the 7-0 League victory over Gillingham during September 2008?

346. Who inflicted Town's first home League defeat of 2-1 of the season during October 2008?

347. Who came on as a substitute to score the equaliser in the 1-1 draw at Brentford in October 2008?

348. Grant Holt's last minute penalty against which team secured a 2-1 win to stay in the top two at the end of November 2008?

349. Town's first goalless draw came against which club after 17 League games?

350. Who was the first Town player to see red in the League during November 2008?

LEAGUE GOALSCORERS – 2

Match the player with the number of League goals he scored for Shrewsbury Town

351.	Mark Atkins	18
352.	Darren Tinson	3
353.	Jake Sedgemore	6
354.	Gavin Cowan	28
355.	Derek Price	7
356.	Glynn Hurst	1
357.	John Manning	54
358.	Carl Griffiths	10
359.	Colin McMenamin	3
360.	Mark Stallard	1

POSITIONS IN THE LEAGUE – 2

Match the position Shrewsbury Town finished to the season

361.	1997/1998	1st
362.	1996/1997	13th
363.	1995/1996	9th
364.	1994/1995	11th
365.	1993/1994	22nd
366.	1992/1993	18th
367.	1991/1992	18th
368.	1990/1991	22nd
369.	1989/1990	22nd
370.	1988/1989	18th

DAVID MOYES

371. David was just 18 when he played for Celtic against which powerhouse in the European Cup?

372. Aged 24, Shrewsbury Town signed the centre-half from which club for £30,000?

373. David established himself as a centre-half, a position that was vacated by which player who also went on to become a reputable coach?

374. After three seasons as a regular, David shocked the Gay Meadow faithful by leaving to join which Scottish club on a free transfer?

375. David finished his playing days and started his managerial career at which club in 1998?

376. Following on from the previous question, which former Shrewsbury manager did David take over from at the club?

377. Who did David replace as manager of Everton in 2002?

378. Who scored the winning goal for Shrewsbury when they defeated Everton in the 2003 FA Cup Third Round upset?

379. David will want to forget a run of three matches during 1988/89 when playing for Preston North End, what happened?

380. What is the profession of David's brother Kenny?

2002/2003

381. True or false: the club finished bottom of the League and were relegated?

382. Which forward finished the club's highest League scorer with 16 goals in 36 starts?

383. Following on from the previous question, can you name the striker who also got double figures, with 11 League goals in 38 starts and two substitute appearances?

384. Which team did The Shrews beat 1-0 at home on the opening day of the League season?

385. Which midfielder scored in the 3-1 home win against Cambridge United during November 2002, with Nigel Jemson scoring a brace in the game?

386. True or false: The Shrews lost their last eight League matches of the season?

387. Which forward scored a hat-trick for The Shrews in the 3-1 home win against Bury on Boxing Day 2002?

388. Which London club did Shrewsbury Town beat 2-0 away during February 2003 with Darren Moss and Matt Redmile scoring?

389. Which manager left the club during April 2003, with Mark Atkins taking over as manager for a month?

390. How many of the club's 46 League matches did they win?

GAY MEADOW

391. ***In which year did Town move to the Gay Meadow 'Fields'?***

392. ***Following on from the previous question, who did Town play in their first League match at the new ground?***

393. ***Gay Meadow's first permanent stand was opened in 1922 having cost how much money to erect?***

394. ***How many gallons of water were estimated to have been covering the pitch 'up to the crossbars' in the 1946 season flooding?***

395. ***Gay Meadow hosted an amateur international in 1952 when England beat who 8-3?***

396. ***What was the Technical College Terrace (and later Duffill Terrace) better known as?***

397. ***In what year did the Gay Meadow first turn on its floodlights – 1957, 1959 or 1961?***

398. ***In July 1963, what popular sport was hosted at Gay Meadow but failed to win the support of the Shrewsbury public?***

399. ***In which year did the Riverside become fully covered?***

400. ***Town's final game at the Gay Meadow during May 2006 was against which club in a 0-0 draw?***

FOURTH DIVISION RUNNERS-UP – 1974/1975

401. ***Town's promotion followed how many seasons in the bottom tier?***

402. ***Who was Town's manager during this successful season?***

403. ***Who beat Town to the title and finished champions?***

404. ***Town enjoyed a run of how many away games unbeaten mid-season before losing to Mansfield Town – 11, 12 or 13??***

405. ***Who did Town beat 7-4 during February 1975?***

406. ***Who was the ever-present goalkeeper during this season?***

407. ***Who topped The Shrews scoring charts for the season with 21 League goals?***

408. ***How many players featured in all 46 league games that season?***

409. ***Despite the League form, Town fell early in the FA Cup to non-League Wigan managed at that time by which future Town manager?***

410. ***Town had clinched promotion before losing 2-1 on the final day to which team?***

DEBUTS

411. *Which player, aged 16 years and 175 days, marked his debut as Town's youngest player in a 3-1 League Cup win over Newport in 1961?*

412. *Which legend and later manager made his Town debut following a £30,000 move from Chester in a 2-2 draw with Oldham in January 1973?*

413. *Which long serving striker came off the bench during February 1983 for a goal scoring debut in the 3-2 defeat at Leicester City?*

414. *Which goal scorer scored on all three debuts for various levels, youth, reserve and first team, at Town in the late 1970s?*

415. *Which England World Cup winner made a guest debut for Town in an exhibition match against Zambia in October 1978?*

416. *Carl Griffiths made his first League appearance for Town away from home at which club during October 1988?*

417. *Which midfield playmaker made his first Town start away at Hull during February 1989?*

418. *Which flying winger made his debut at Grimsby in August 1983 and became almost ever-present for four seasons?*

419. *In what year did Jake King make his Shrewsbury debut against Rochdale?*

420. *Which defender made his first appearance midway through the 1993/94 season; forging a championship winning partnership with Mark Williams?*

THE WELSH CUP

421. How many times have Town won the Welsh Cup?

422. How many times have Town lost in a Welsh Cup final?

423. Why did Bernard McNally miss out on the Welsh Cup final second leg victory over Bangor City?

424. In what year did Shrewsbury last appear in the Welsh Cup?

425. Who did Shrewsbury beat in their last Welsh Cup match before being eliminated because Ron Green was ineligible?

426. Who beat Town in their first ever Welsh Cup match?

427. Town beat Wrexham 5-2 to win their first Welsh Cup in which year?

428. What was the name of the player who netted a club record of seven goals in the 21-0 record victory against Mold at the end of the 19th Century?

429. In which year did Town last win the Welsh Cup beating Bangor City?

430. Following on from the previous question, which Welsh based team did The Shrews beat in the final the previous year?

LEAGUE APPEARANCES – 2

Match the player to the number of League appearances he made for Shrewsbury Town

431.	Colin Whitaker	*304 (2)*
432.	Gary Stevens	*158 (3)*
433.	David Tong	*144*
434.	John Moore	*65*
435.	David Pleat	*156 (4)*
436.	Jake King	*152*
437.	John Hudson	*1*
438.	Ross MacLaren	*144 (6)*
439.	Alan Brown	*48*
440.	Brian Coyne	*10 (2)*

CONFERENCE PLAY-OFF WINNERS – 2003/2004

441. Which team did Shrewsbury Town beat in the play-off final?

442. What was the score after extra time – 1-1, 2-1 or 3-1?

443. Which forward scored for The Shrews in the 43rd minute of the game?

444. Where was the final game played?

445. Can you name the goalkeeper that played in the final for Town?

446. What was the attendance in the final – 18, 216, 19,216 or 20,216?

447. Which Shrews manager guided the club to this success?

448. In which position did The Shrews finish in the Conference – second, third or fourth?

449. Which team did Shrewsbury beat in the play-off semi-finals, with the score being 2-2 after two legs and then went on to beat them 5-3 on penalties at Gay Meadow?

450. True or false: the club were unbeaten in their last five League matches?

VICTOR KASULE

451. ***During Victor's time at Town, which club was he loaned to in 1989?***

452. ***Which team-mate's car did Victor allegedly write-off driving to an off-licence after training in 1989?***

453. ***Which manager signed winger Victor in 1987?***

454. ***How much did Shrewsbury pay Meadowbank Thistle for Victor's services when he joined Town?***

455. ***What title did Victor win in a BBC poll for Albion Rovers with 55% of the votes?***

456. ***What happened to Victor during one acrobatic goal celebration at the Gay Meadow?***

457. ***On returning to Scotland, Victor's off-field antics earned him what catchy nickname?***

458. ***Victor was allegedly booked during a match in 1989 while playing for Chesterfield for doing what to a referee?***

459. ***Victor's mother was Scottish but his father ensured he qualified to play for which African country?***

460. ***During a match at Bradford in 1988, Victor became the first Shrewsbury player to do what?***

HAT-TRICKS

461. Steve Biggins' only League hat-trick came in a 3-1 win over which close rivals in 1979?

462. Who scored an eight-minute hat-trick in the 1983 5-1 League victory over Leeds United?

463. Which player scored two hat-tricks in the first eight League games during Shrewsbury's great start to the 1984/85 season?

464. Which player bagged a hat-trick in his 100th appearance in the penultimate game of the 1990/1991 season?

465. Which player scored five hat-tricks; a four and a club equalling seven goals on his way to 35 goals in 1946?

466. Arthur Rowley's second goal of three against Port Vale on the opening day of the 1961 season saw him pass which milestone?

467. A hat-trick each against Bristol Rovers in 1962 for Jimmy McLaughlin and which other player who later became a prominent manager, was the only time two players have completed trebles for Town in the same League match?

468. Who scored Town's quickest ever hat-trick in four minutes and 32 seconds from first goal to last in 1990 against Bradford City?

469. A hat-trick by which player against Halifax saw him draw level with Arthur Rowley's single season scoring record in 1973?

470. Who scored the only League hat-trick for Town in the 1989/90 season against Huddersfield Town?

CHIC BATES

471. Chic's name was used in the lyrics of the song 'For Skinny Indie Kids' by which strangely named Indie band?

472. How many spells at Shrewsbury did Chic have as manager?

473. Who did Chic replace as caretaker-manager on a match-to-match basis in 2004?

474. Who did Chic replace as manager in 1984?

475. Chic's first spell in charge lasted until 1987, but who replaced him?

476. Which is the only other League club Chic has managed?

477. Chic replaced the man who initially hired him as assistant at Stoke City, can you name him?

478. Which player, now famous as a Sky sports pundit, replaced Chic as manager of Stoke City in 1998?

479. From which club did Chic return to the Gay Meadow for £20,000 during 1979/80?

480. Who resigned as Town chairman after fellow directors had demanded he sack Chic?

MATCH THE YEAR – 2

Match up the year to the event

481.	The club was founded	2007
482.	The club won the Third Division title for the first time in their history	1990
483.	Harry Gregg took over as manager of Shrewsbury Town	1910
484.	Grant Holt was born	1968
485.	Michael Jackson joined Town from Blackpool	1886
486.	The club reached the first ever play-off final at the new Wembley Stadium	1968
487.	Bournemouth scored against Town after just eight seconds	2007
488.	Asa Hartford took over as manager of Shrewsbury Town	2008
489.	Marc Pugh joined Town from Bury	1979
490.	The club moved to Gay Meadow	1981

DAVID EDWARDS

491. Born in Shrewsbury, but in which town did David grow up?

492. David's Shrewsbury debut was made in which unfor gettable match as a second half substitute in 2003?

493. David was left out of Shrewsbury's 2007 League Two play-off final defeat against Bristol Rovers for what reason?

494. What was the alleged fee agreed for David when he moved to Luton Town in 2007?

495. Why did Luton Town sell David to Wolves for £675,000 after only 19 games?

496. David scored on his Wolves debut against who?

497. David decided not to play for the country of his birth place and has instead represented which country?

498. Against which European powerhouse did David make his international debut in a 0-0 away draw in 2007?

499. Who did David score his first international goal against in 2008?

500. What squad number did David wear whilst a Shrewsbury player?

JOHN McGINLAY

501. ***Which Shrewsbury manager signed John on a tip off from his son without ever watching him play?***

502. ***How old was John when he made his first senior appearance for his native Fort William?***

503. ***Which then non-League side did John first get his taste of English football with for three seasons?***

504. ***Who was the manager in charge that made the unpopular decision to sell John to Bury in 1990 – just 18 months after he had arrived?***

505. ***Following on from the previous question, Bury paid a then club record fee to sign him, but for how much?***

506. ***John later became a legend at Bolton Wanderers, and was voted what in 2003?***

507. ***Arguably, John's finest goal came for Scotland against which country to help book them a passage to World Cup 1998 with a 1-0 win.***

508. ***Who was John playing for in 1991 when he scored a hat-trick against Bolton Wanderers, securing a move there several months later?***

509. ***Which rising star did John first strike a partnership with at Shrewsbury Town?***

510. ***Which country did John finish his playing days in and later took up a coaching role?***

THE PROSTAR STADIUM

511. What was the name of Shrewsbury's previous stadium?

512. In which month in 2007 did the stadium open?

513. Which construction company built this new stadium?

514. What is the capacity of this stadium – 8,875, 9,875 or 10, 875?

515. The majority of seats at the stadium are blue, but what colour seats are the initials STFC?

516. Which team did The Shrews play in their first ever match at the new stadium in a 4-0 friendly win?

517. Following on from the previous question, which Shrewsbury player was the first player to score at the new stadium in the friendly match?

518. Which team did Shrewsbury play their first competitive match at the new stadium in the League Cup in a 1-0 win?

519. Following on from the previous question, who scored the only goal in the game in extra time?

520. True or false: The Shrews won their first League game at the new stadium, winning 1-0 with Dave Hibbert scoring a penalty against Bradford City?

PETER WILDING

521. ***Peter was signed by Jake King from Telford in 1997, but where did the pair link up prior to joining Telford 18 months earlier?***

522. ***The versatile Peter played in nearly every position, even goalkeeper when replacing who with an injury in December 1998?***

523. ***What was the fee Shrewsbury paid their local rivals Telford for Peter's services?***

524. ***Which rising star did Peter mark out of the game in a famous FA Cup victory in the 2002/2003 season?***

525. ***Which former Shrewsbury goalkeeper who went on to play for Chelsea is Peter's Godfather?***

526. ***Why did Peter's mother miss watching the FA Cup clash with Chelsea in 2003?***

527. ***Who was the manager when Peter declined a new contract to return to semi-professional football?***

528. ***Which club did Peter join in 2003 before retiring shortly after?***

529. ***What job was Peter doing before Jake King took him to Telford in 1996?***

530. ***Still a popular figure in his home town, Pete 'the Feet' is now doing what profession in Shrewsbury?***

POSITIONS IN THE LEAGUE – 3

Match the position Shrewsbury Town finished to the season

531.	1987/1988	9th
532.	1986/1987	1st
533.	1985/1986	18th
534.	1984/1985	14th
535.	1983/1984	18th
536.	1982/1983	8th
537.	1981/1982	13th
538.	1980/1981	8th
539.	1979/1980	18th
540.	1978/1979	17th

2004/2005

541. *In which position did The Shrews finish in the League?*

542. *Which two players signed for the club on free transfers from Preston North End during December 2004?*

543. *Which team did The Shrews draw 0-0 with at home on the last day of the season?*

544. *Can you name the three managers who managed the club during this season?*

545. *Which team did Shrewsbury beat 5-0 at home during February 2005?*

546. *True or false: The Shrews were unbeaten in the League during January 2005?*

547. *Can you name the two players who finished the club's top League scorers, both with six goals apiece?*

548. *How many of the club's 46 League matches did they win – 11, 14 or 17?*

549. *Which goalkeeper played in 40 of the club's 46 League matches during this season?*

550. *Which forward left for Grimsby during September 2004?*

GREAT ESCAPE – EXETER V SHREWSBURY – MAY 2000

551. ***What was the final score as Shrewsbury escaped relegation on the final day of the season?***

552. ***Which two rivals lost to ensure Town stayed in the football League?***

553. ***Which team was eventually relegated?***

554. ***Who was Town's manager at the time?***

555. ***Mickey Brown got the vital goal, but who had he replaced as substitute earlier?***

556. ***In which minute did Exeter pull one back?***

557. ***What is the name of Exeter's ground?***

558. ***What was the name of the Exeter goalkeeper credited with an own goal opener?***

559. ***Who was the former Town manager in charge of the Chester City side that went down?***

560. ***Defeat at home to which club preceded the Great Escape?***

LEAGUE GOALSCORERS – 3

Match the player with the number of League goals he scored for Shrewsbury Town

561.	Eric Brodie	65
562.	Austin Berkley	38
563.	Peter Dolby	12
564.	Roger Preece	35
565.	Paul Maguire	3
566.	David Poutney	3
567.	David Hughes	22
568.	Graham Turner	21
569.	Lee Steele	24
570.	Alf Wood	11

THIRD DIVISION CHAMPIONS – 1993/1994

571. Who was the new chairman at the helm for the 1993/94 season?

572. Town endured a dreadful start which included a 6-1 drubbing at where in the third game?

573. Who scored the club's fastest ever goal after 14 seconds against Bury at home?

574. Carl Griffiths scored his last goal for Town before his transfer to Manchester City against who?

575. Which Northern Ireland international formed a solid centre half partnership with Dave Walton during this season?

576. Who picked up the Player of the Year award?

577. Town's triumph was forged by a tremendous mid season run of how many games unbeaten?

578. After finishing top scorer in all competitions, which player was named in the season's League XI team?

579. Despite a defeat and draw in their last two games, Town clinched the title by how many points?

580. Who finished runners-up?

1970s

581. *Who scored Town's first ever Second Division goal in a 1-1 draw with Notts County in 1979?*

582. *To bolster their Division Two squad, which player did Town splash a record £100,000 on in 1979?*

583. *'Coracle Man' Fred Davies made history in 1971 season by doing what?*

584. *Which player broke Arthur Rowley's single season scoring record with 40 goals in the 1971/72 season?*

585. *Which season saw Town promoted back to the old Third Division after finishing runners-up?*

586. *Which manager resigned at the start of the 1972/73 season?*

587. *Which national team did Town beat 3-1 in a 1976 pre-season friendly?*

588. *How many full time managers did Shrewsbury have in the 1970s?*

589. *Which midfielder played in every single League, FA Cup and Welsh Cup game in the 1976/77 season?*

590. *Town endured a miserable end to the 1972/73 season by scoring one goal in how many matches?*

WAYNE CLARKE

591. Although joining full time in 1993, Wayne spent a spell on loan at Shrewsbury from which club in 1990?

592. Wayne bagged a hat-trick against which Midlands club during that 1990 loan spell in a 4-1 win?

593. With which club did Wayne win a First Division Championship medal after scoring five goals in 10 matches?

594. Wayne's goals in his first season led Shrewsbury to which title in 1994?

595. Wayne's single goal for Everton in a 1-0 win over Liverpool was notable for what reason in 1987?

596. Shrewsbury signed Wayne from which West Midlands club in 1993?

597. Wayne is one of how many brothers that have played professional football?

598. Who did Wayne join as player-manager after leaving The Shrews in 1995?

599. Who was the manager that signed Wayne for Shrewsbury?

600. At which level did Wayne represent England?

WHERE DID THEY GO – 2

Match up the player with the team they joined after leaving Shrewsbury Town

601.	Darran Kempson	Halifax Town
602.	Derek Asamoah	Sheffield United
603.	Sagi Burton	Wrexham
604.	Danny Hall	Lincoln City
605.	Colin Murdock	Northwich Victoria
606.	Mark Stallard	Gretna
607.	Colin McMenamin	Accrington
608.	Mark Cartwright	Gretna
609.	Stephen Jagielka	Nice
610.	Greg Rioch	Barnet

NIGEL JEMSON

611. ***As one of the game's hottest young strikers, Nigel joined which manager at Nottingham Forest who allegedly remarked: "Jemson is the one man in football with a bigger head than me!"?***

612. ***Which under-fire manager did Nigel allegedly claim he would make him pay with his job for not signing him when Forest played them in the FA Cup in 1990?***

613. ***Who did Nigel join from Forest for nearly one million pounds?***

614. ***Nigel scored the winner at Wembley when his Forest side beat who in the 1990 League Cup final?***

615. ***Nigel's return to Wembley in 1996 saw his Rotherham side beat Shrewsbury 2-1 in the Auto Windscreens final, but in what minute did his second goal come?***

616. ***How many goals did Nigel notch up during his first season for The Shrews – 12, 15 or 18?***

617. ***In Town's famous 2003 FA Cup win over Everton, who was fouled for Nigel to score the first goal with a superb free-kick?***

618. ***Who later provided the cross from a free-kick for Nigel's winner?***

619. ***Trailing 4-0, Nigel scored a memorable eight-minute hat-trick for The Shrews after coming off the bench against which club during August 2002?***

620. ***Pre-Shrewsbury, one of the clubs Nigel joined briefly was in Scotland. Can you name it?***

KEVIN SUMMERFIELD

621. Kevin ended his playing days with Shrewsbury to take up which role at the club?

622. Kevin has gone on to form a successful partnership with which manager at four clubs?

623. At which club has Kevin been caretaker-manager on two occasions, during 1999/2000 for five matches and then again during 2003/2004 for nine matches?

624. How many League games did Kevin play in for Shrewsbury in his career?

625. How many appearances did Kevin make for England's Youth Team?

626. During which season did Kevin make his Town debut?

627. Kevin joined Shrewsbury Town from which south coast club during September 1990?

628. Kevin spent a brief spell in 1984 playing for which non-English club?

629. Kevin caused a storm by following Paul Sturrock to which club as assistant manager from Plymouth Argyle?

630. How much did Kevin cost The Shrews when he signed for Shrewsbury Town?

2007/2008

631. Which team did Shrewsbury beat 4-0 away from home on the opening day of the League season?

632. Following on from the previous season, which forward scored a brace in the game?

633. Which team did Shrewsbury beat 3-1 at home on Boxing Day 2007?

634. Which manager took over in March 2008 from Gary Peters?

635. In which position did the club finish in League Two?

636. Who finished the club's highest League scorer with 12 goals during this season?

637. Can you name the two scorers who scored in the 2-0 home win against Morecambe during January 2008?

638. How many League goals did Ben Davies score during this season?

639. Who scored the only goal for The Shrews in the 1-0 away win against Wrexham during November 2007?

640. True or false: Shrewsbury were unbeaten in the League during April 2008?

CARL GRIFFITHS

641. Carl made a blistering start to his Shrewsbury scoring career with his first two goals against which club?

642. Following on from the previous question, the next game, Carl scored another two against who?

643. Carl's early goal exploits were hailed by the tabloids who said he could be Britain's first what?

644. After intense publicity, Carl was dropped to be shielded from the media by which manager?

645. After Carl's healthy goal ratio for Shrewsbury Town, which club paid up £450,000 for his services in 1993?

646. Following on from the previous question, which well-known player moved to the club shortly after his transfer and then followed him to Portsmouth, restricting his appearances for both clubs?

647. In 2005, Carl made a return to the Gay Meadow with which side that lost 4-1 in the FA Cup to The Shrews?

648. Which former club of Carl's finished runners-up in the 2008 Masters Tournament to Wolves?

649. Carl applied for the vacant Town manager's job after who got fired stating: "I'd love to come back in the future."?

650. Who was Carl's final League club, playing his last game for them in 2003?

THIRD DIVISION CHAMPIONS – 1978/1979

651. Who was manager for the start of The Shrews' championship winning season?

652. Following on from the previous question, who took over the manager's post after being promoted from within for his first managerial job?

653. Who did Town beat on the final day of the season to clinch promotion?

654. Following on from the previous question, what was the score that clinched promotion?

655. The League run was complimented by another impressive FA Cup run when they claimed the scalp of which high flying Division One side?

656. How many years did Shrewsbury enjoy in the old Division Two?

657. Who were Town chasing in the run-in for the title?

658. Who was the only player to feature in every single League match?

659. Which player (and later manager) scored three goals in the final two games of the season?

660. Who finished Town's top scorer with 13 League goals?

WHO AM I? – 2

661. ***I am a forward and was born in 1986. I signed from Preston North End in June 2007 and finished the club's highest League scorer in my first season.***

662. ***I hold the club record for making the most League appearances for Shrewsbury Town Football Club.***

663. ***I was a striker and played for the club between 2006 and 2008, I signed from Bradford City and scored a hat-trick in my third match for the club.***

664. ***I was born in 1985, I spent a month on loan at The Shrews before signing on a free transfer in 2004 from Preston North End.***

665. ***I was born in December 1967, I played as a defender and played for Shrewsbury Town from 1985 until 1989, when I left the club I joined Wolves.***

666. ***I had three spells at the club, the first spell was from 1986 until 1991, I then joined Bolton Wanderers before coming back to Shrewsbury in December 1992, I was born in 1968 and played as a forward.***

667. ***I won 34 Northern Ireland caps in my career, I played as a defender and I played for Shrewsbury between 1992 and 1995, I made 103 League appearances for the club, scoring three goals.***

668. ***I signed for The Shrews in 1998, having spent 10 years at Chester, I am a defender who was born in Liverpool, I made 25 League appearances for Shrewsbury Town.***

669. ***I am an Irish defender and signed for The Shrews in the summer of 2008, I scored on my Shrews debut against Macclesfield Town at home.***

670. ***I signed for Colchester United on 2 January 2009, I am a defender and made 79 League appearances, scoring one goal for The Shrews.***

HONOURS

Match up the title to the year Shrewsbury Town were placed

671.	League Cup semi-finalists	1994
672.	Third Division Champions	1996
673.	Fourth Division runners-up	1980
674.	Conference play-off winners	1985
675.	League Two finalists	1979
676.	Welsh Cup winners	2003
677.	Football League Trophy runners-up	2004
678.	Welsh Cup winners	2007
679.	Football League Trophy area finalists	1961
680.	Third Division Champions	1975

MICKEY BROWN

681. Mickey holds the record for making the most appearances for the club with how many games – 318, 418 or 518?

682. How many spells has Mickey had for Shrewsbury?

683. Mickey's first spell ended in 1991 with an unsuccessful move to which club, before returning to Gay Meadow a year later?

684. In 1996, Mickey was loaned back to Shrewsbury Town before joining for his final spell from which club?

685. Mickey's goal during the infamous 'Great Escape' match against Exeter in May 2000, when The Shrews escaped relegation from the League, came after he was brought on as a substitute after how many minutes?

686. Following on from the previous question, who provided the cross for Mickey's crucial goal?

687. Who did Mickey join after his final stint ended in 2001?

688. Later on, Mickey joined the League of Wales club formerly managed by ex-Shrews boss Jake King. Who was it?

689. As well as being a fitness instructor, Mickey took on what unusual job post-football?

690. Mickey has been bestowed with which unofficial hon our by many Shrewsbury Town fans?

2005/2006

691. Who was The Shrews manager during this season?

692. Who was the club's highest scorer with 10 League goals?

693. Following on from the previous question, can you name the forward that was one goal behind, finishing with nine League goals in his 42 League appearances?

694. How many games did it take before Shrewsbury won their first game of the season – five, six or seven?

695. Following on from the previous question, can you name the London team that Shrewsbury beat 1-0 during August 2005 to record their first League win of the season?

696. In which position did Shrewsbury Town finish in the League?

697. Who scored a brace for Shrewsbury in the 4-1 home win against Rushden & Diamonds during April 2006?

698. Which team came back to beat Shrewsbury 4-3 on Boxing Day 2005, Shrewsbury were 3-1 up at half time?

699. Which Welsh based team did Shrewsbury beat 2-1 away during April 2006 with Colin McMenamin scoring a penalty and the other being an own goal?

700. Who scored The Shrews only goal in the 1-0 away win on the final day of the season against Chester City?

POT LUCK – 1

701. In 1983, Magistrates withdrew what from Shrewsbury Town?

702. Shrewsbury won a trophy in which sport thanks to an inspirational display from goalkeeper Steve Ogrizovic in 1983?

703. In 1985, what was installed at Gay Meadow for the first time?

704. Who were Town scheduled to play in 1987 to celebrate the centenary but it never took place?

705. In 1988, which former secretary director was quoted as saying he wanted football hooligans 'flogged' after a spate of violence?

706. Mickey Thomas scored his only Shrewsbury goal in an away win against which Midlands club during March 1989?

707. Which famous commentator had an unsuccessful trial during Arthur Rowley's management days?

708. The quickest goal scored against Town came after how many seconds in 1968?

709. Which former player and his father are the only father and son to have played for the England Youth Team?

710. Which race horse owner adopted Town's blue and yel low stripes as his racing colours after the promotion winning 1979 season?

LEAGUE APPEARANCES – 3

Match the player to the number of League appearances he made for Shrewsbury Town

711.	John Parr	342 (13)
712.	David Linighan	110 (34)
713.	John McGinlay	76
714.	Wayne Clarke	34 (3)
715.	David Geddis	65
716.	Carl Griffiths	58 (2)
717.	Steve Ogrizovic	34 (1)
718.	Graham Turner	112
719.	Darren Hughes	84
720.	Alan Groves	36 (3)

POT LUCK – 2

721. ***Groundsman Brian Perry also played cricket for Shropshire and caught and bowled which legendary batsmen during their game with Yorkshire in 1984?***

722. ***Former chairman Ray Bailey represented England at which sport?***

723. ***Why was Town's opening season game in 1991/92 postponed by 24 hours?***

724. ***Which player became Shrewsbury's first non-white captain in 1994?***

725. ***While Fred Davies was known as one of Town's most popular managers, what was his namesake also more commonly known as?***

726. ***What was significant about the Wales v Ireland inter national match in 1890?***

727. ***Actor Harry Shearer immortalised Town's kit by wearing it in which 1980s' film?***

728. ***Which former Town centre-half married former glam our model Lindsey Dawn Mackenzie in 2006?***

729. ***Town's theme tune of 'Catch us if you can' is sung by which group?***

730. ***A 3-1 win at Brierley Hill Alliance brought to an end Town's worst run of how many away defeats in 1902?***

GARY PETERS

731. Gary became Shrewsbury Town manager after scouting for which former Shrewsbury star-cum-manager from June 2003 until November 2004?

732. As a player, Gary made his most number of appearances for which club between 1975 and 1979?

733. Following on from the previous question, which other club did Gary play for twice during his career, from 1979 until 1982 and then again in 1988 until 1990?

734. Gary made his mark as a manager with which club between 1994-98?

735. When did Gary become manager of Shrewsbury?

736. Following on from the previous question, from whom did he take over?

737. Following on from the previous question, after keeping them up in his first season, what position did Shrewsbury finish in after his second season in charge (2005/06)?

738. Gary finally left the club as manager after a run of 12 games that spawned how many points?

739. Gary's final game in charge of The Shrews was a 4-1 defeat at where?

740. As manager of Preston, which future England star did Gary famously take on loan?3

WHERE DID THEY COME FROM – 3

Match the player to the club they joined Shrewsbury Town from

741.	Ben Davies	Crewe Alexandra
742.	Sagi Burton	Sheffield Wednesday
743.	Kevin Street	West Ham United
744.	Trevor Challis	Peterborough United
745.	Ian Dunbavin	Bristol Rovers
746.	Spencer Whelan	Telford
747.	Darren Currie	Bury
748.	Darren Rowbotham	Chester City
749.	Ian Stevens	Chester City
750.	Mark Taylor	Liverpool

1960s

751. Town's match with Hull in 1961 was twice in doubt due to an outbreak of what?

752. In early 1963, what half time entertainment was introduced for the fans?

753. Shrewsbury conducted their first ever overseas pre-season tour in 1964 to which East European country?

754. 3,000 fans watched Town record an FA Cup win against which London team that was in the middle of a 59-game unbeaten League run in 1965?

755. Arthur Rowley's last game for Shrewsbury Town came in the 2-1 final day defeat to which club in 1965?

756. On 24 August 1965, Tony Gregory made history doing what?

757. Which player did Shrewsbury sign from Luton Town in 1967 who later became a well known Luton manager?

758. On the final day of the 1968 season, Town missed out on promotion to Division Two by one point to which team?

759. Which former Busby Babe succeeded Arthur Rowley as manager in July 1968?

760. In 1969, which player opened the famous Salopian Sports shop?

SQUAD NUMBERS – 2008/2009 – 2

Match up the player with his Shrewsbury Town squad number

761.	David Hunt	15
762.	Michael Jackson	22
763.	Glyn Garner	6
764.	Jasbir Singh	17
765.	David Maguire	16
766.	Marc Tierney	24
767.	Grant Holt	4
768.	Paul Murray	23
769.	Shane Cansdell-Sherriff	30
770.	Chris Humphrey	1

WHERE DID THEY GO – 3

Match up the player with the team they joined after leaving Shrewsbury Town

771.	Austin Berkley	Exeter City
772.	Roger Preece	Crewe Alexandra
773.	Devon White	Hereford United
774.	Darren Rowbotham	Doncaster Rovers
775.	Steve Anthrobus	Wycombe Wanderers
776.	Mark Williams	Fulham
777.	O'Neill Donaldson	Ilkeston Town
778.	Mark Blake	Telford
779.	Gary Patterson	Barnet
780.	Howard Clark	Chesterfield Town

BIG WINS – 2

Match up the game to the final score

781.	v. Aldershot (home), 2 February 1952, League	4-0
782.	v. Watford (home), August 1953, League	6-2
783.	v. Swindon Town (home), May 1955, League	5-0
784.	v. Norwich City (home), August 1955, League	6-2
785.	v. Swindon Town (home), December 1956, League	7-0
786.	v. Southport (home), December 1958, League	7-2
787.	v. Accrington Stanley (home), August 1959, League	5-1
788.	v. Chelmsford City (away), November 1962, FA Cup 1st round	6-0
789.	v. Luton Town (away), March 1965, League	7-3
790.	v. Scunthorpe United (home), April 1968, League	6-4

LEAGUE TWO PLAY-OFF FINALISTS – 2006/2007

791. Which team beat Shrewsbury 3-1 in the play-off final?

792. Which midfielder scored for The Shrews in the play-off final?

793. Which Town defender got sent off in the final in the 89th minute?

794. At which stadium was the final played?

795. What was the attendance at the play-off final – 59,589, 60,589 or 61,589?

796. In which position did Shrewsbury finish in the League – fifth, sixth or seventh?

797. How many of Town's 46 League matches did they win – 16, 18 or 20?

798. Which manager guided Shrewsbury Town to the play-off final?

799. Which team did Shrewsbury beat 5-0 at home during August 2006, which was the club's biggest League win of the season?

800. True or false: Shrewsbury were unbeaten in their seven League games during March 2007?

ANSWERS

HISTORY OF THE CLUB

1. *Salop or The Shrews*
2. *1886*
3. *Midland League*
4. *Arthur Rowley*
5. *The Auto Windscreens Shield Final*
6. *Blue and amber strips*
7. *Mickey Brown*
8. *1961*
9. *Graham Turner*
10. *7-0*

NATIONALITIES – 1

11.	*Guy Madjo*	*Cameroonian*
12.	*Ben Davies*	*English*
13.	*Darren Moss*	*Welsh*
14.	*Shane Cansdell-Sherriff*	*Australian*
15.	*James Meredith*	*Australian*
16.	*Derek Asamoah*	*Ghanaian*
17.	*Jimmy Quinn*	*Northern Irish*
18.	*Paul Evans*	*Welsh*
19.	*Graham Turner*	*English*
20.	*Wayne Clarke*	*English*

1990s

21. *Fred Davies*
22. *13*
23. *Ian Stevens*
24. *Lee Steele (13 goals), Richard Scott (10 goals) and Devon White (10 goals)*
25. *Mark Taylor*
26. *Asa Hartford*
27. *62 points*
28. *Darren Currie*
29. *Steve Kerrigan*
30. *14*

SQUAD NUMBERS – 2008/2009 – 1

31.	Ben Davies	14
32.	Marc Pugh	7
33.	Kelvin Langmead	8
34.	Neil Ashton	3
35.	Guy Madjo	19
36.	Ben Herd	12
37.	Steven Hindmarch	20
38.	Dave Hibbert	9
39.	Michael Symes	11
40.	Darren Moss	2

WHERE DID THEY COME FROM – 1

41.	Russell Crossley	Liverpool
42.	Alan Durban	Derby County
43.	Grant Holt	Nottingham Forest
44.	Shane Cansdell-Sherriff	Tranmere Rovers
45.	Howard Clark	Coventry City
46.	Graham Clapham	Newcastle United
47.	Graham Coughlan	Rotherham United
48.	John Keay	Celtic
49.	Paul Wimbleton	Bristol City
50.	Barry Stobart	Aston Villa

MANAGERS

51.	Alan Durban	1974-1978
52.	John Bond	1991-1993
53.	Jimmy Quinn	2003-2004
54.	Gary Peters	2004-2008
55.	Kevin Ratcliffe	1999-2003
56.	Harry Gregg	1968-1972
57.	Chic Bates	1984-1987
58.	Jake King	1997-1999
59.	Sammy Crooks	1950-1954
60.	Fred Davies	1993-1997

INTERNATIONALS

61.	Sandy Brown	1 Scotland Cap

62.	Mark Williams	36 Northern Ireland Caps
63.	Nigel Jemson	1 England Under-21 Cap
64.	Mickey Thomas	51 Wales Caps
65.	Scott Howie	5 Scotland Under-21 Caps
66.	Doug Rougvie	1 Scotland Cap
67.	John McGinlay	13 Scotland Caps
68.	Jimmy Quinn	48 Northern Ireland Caps
69.	Paul Evans	2 Wales Caps
70.	Joe Hart	5 England Under-19 Caps

LEAGUE APPEARANCES – 1

71.	George Boardman	172 (4)
72.	Wayne Williams	212 (9)
73.	Peter Wall	18
74.	Chic Bates	274 (20)
75.	Anthony Kelly	100 (1)
76.	Neil Lyne	77 (3)
77.	Alan Finley	60 (3)
78.	David Moyes	91 (5)
79.	Harry Middleton	85
80.	Colin Robinson	176 (18)

THE LEAGUE CUP

81. David Batty
82. Diomansy Kamara (59 minutes)
83. Semi-final (lost to Rotherham)
84. Kevin Summerfield
85. Cardiff City
86. First (losing to Stockport County 3-2 on aggregate)
87. 7: 1970/1971, 1972/1973, 1973/1974, 1974/1975, 1976/1977, 1977/1978 and 1978/1979
88. Four
89. 1986/87
90. Carlisle United

GOALKEEPERS

91. 1981
92. Steve Ogrizovic

93. Jo Hart

94. Fred Boxley

95. Paul Miller

96. Mike Walker

97. Scott Howie

98. Ken Mulhearn

99. Steve Perks

100. Paul Edwards

POSITIONS IN THE LEAGUE – 1

101.	*2007/2008*	*18th*
102.	*2006/2007*	*7th*
103.	*2005/2006*	*10th*
104.	*2004/2005*	*21st*
105.	*2003/2004*	*3rd*
106.	*2002/2003*	*24th*
107.	*2001/1002*	*9th*
108.	*2000/2001*	*15th*
109.	*1999/2000*	*22nd*
110.	*1998/1999*	*15th*

ATTENDANCES

111. *1979/80*

112. *Ipswich*

113. *12,356*

114. *400 (Lost 2-1)*

115. *Welsh Cup (beat Swansea Town 2-1 in the replay four months later in September!)*

116. *7.5p*

117. *16,070 (although media reported over 22,000 attended)*

118. *15,000*

119. *As a result of the Taylor report post-Hillsborough (it had only one entrance/exit to terracing)*

120. *Walsall*

BIG WINS – 1

121.	*v. Southport (home), May 1968, League*	*5-1*

122.	*v. Port Vale (home), September 1970, League*	*7-3*
123.	*v. Blackburn Rovers (home), October 1971, League*	*7-1*
124.	*v. Colchester United (away), November 1971, FA Cup 1st round*	*4-1*
125.	*v. Welshpool (home), December 1973, Welsh Cup*	*5-0*
126.	*v. Llanidloes (home), December 1974, Welsh Cup*	*9-0*
127.	*v. Doncaster Rovers (home), February 1975, League*	*7-4*
128.	*v. Bury (home), April 1978, League*	*5-3*
129.	*v. Rhyl (home), January 1979, Welsh Cup*	*6-0*
130.	*v. Fulham (home), May 1980, League*	*5-2*

1999/2000

131. *Jake King*

132. *Kevin Ratcliffe*

133. *True (away against Leyton Orient)*

134. *Carlisle United*

135. *Southend United*

136. *3-0 to Shrewsbury Town*

137. *Lee Steele*

138. *Exeter City*

139. *Nine*

140. *13*

WHO AM I? – 1

141. *Glynn Garner*

142. *Maurice Evans*

143. *Ian Atkins*

144. *Kelvin Langmead*

145. *Steve Ogrizovic*

146. *Ian Stevens*

147. Ben Davies

148. Paul Evans

149. Steve Kerrigan

150. Alan Durban

LEAGUE GOALSCORERS – 1

151.	Gary Hackett	17
152.	George Andrews	49
153.	Sagi Burton	5
154.	Frank Clarke	77
155.	Derek Asamoah	10
156.	Paul Petts	16
157.	Colin Murdock	2
158.	Colin Whitaker	59
159.	Ian Atkins	58
160.	Chic Bates	64

THE FA CUP

161. Gary Shaw

162. Michael Thomas (64 minutes)

163. Huddersfield Town (3-0 in third round)

164. 1910 (losing 3-0 at Portsmouth)

165. They drew 1-1 three times before winning the third replay 3-1

166. First time a Town match was all-ticket (17,249 sold)

167. Leeds United (2-0)

168. 11-2

169. Liverpool

170. Leicester City (5-2)

MATCH THE YEAR – 1

171.	Stephen Jagielka made his Shrews League debut	1997
172.	David Hunt was born	1982
173.	Luke Rodgers left Shrewsbury Town and joined Crewe Alexandra	2005
174.	John Bond took over as manager of Shrewsbury Town	1991
175.	Carl Griffiths finished top goal scorer in Division Three	1993

176.	Chris Humphrey made his Shrews League debut	2006
177.	Paul Simpson took over as manager of The Shrews	2008
178.	Nigel Jemson played his last game for Shrewsbury Town	2003
179.	Hereford United beat The Shrews 6-5 in the Welsh Cup semi-final replay	1976
180.	Shane Cansdell-Sherriff was born	1982

1980s

181. 1981/1982
182. 1980/81
183. Wayne Williams
184. Leicester City
185. Bob Hall
186. Gary Hackett
187. Post-Heysel disaster, UEFA banned English clubs from playing abroad
188. Gerry Daly (from Birmingham City)
189. Colin Griffin
190. Ninth

2000/2001

191. 15th
192. Hartlepool United
193. Rochdale
194. Luke Rodgers
195. Nigel Jemson
196. Matt Redmile
197. 15
198. Nigel Jemson
199. Kevin Ratcliffe
200. David Hughes

DEAN SPINK

201. Centre forward
202. John Bond
203. Aston Villa

204. Seven (1990-97)
205. Physiotherapist (youth team and later first team)
206. Wrexham
207. Chester City (with Owen Brown and Andy Porter)
208. All-time cult hero
209. Colwyn Bay
210. Four matches

NATIONALTIES – 2

211.	Sandy Brown	Scottish
212.	Nigel Pearson	English
213.	Graham Coughlan	Irish
214.	John McGinlay	Scottish
215.	Bernard McNally	Northern Irish
216.	Carl Griffiths	Welsh
217.	Ross MacLaren	Scottish
218.	Mark Williams	Northern Irish
219.	Mickey Thomas	Welsh
220.	Ian Woan	English

STEVE ANTHROBUS

221. Millwall
222. £150,000
223. None
224. Phil Babb
225. 12
226. Crewe Alexandra
227. TNS (Total Network Solutions)
228. Hednesford Town (beat Canvey Island 3-2)
229. Dress up as team mascot Pitman Pete!
230. Hednesford Town

SHIRT SPONSORS

231.	1982-86	Link 51
232.	1987-88	Wem Ales
233.	1988-89	Davenports
234.	1990-92	Greenhous
235.	1992-95	WSJ

236.	*1995-97*	*Greenhous*
237.	*1997-99*	*Ternhill Communications*
238.	*1999-05*	*RMW*
239.	*2005-07*	*Morris Lubricants*
240.	*2007-08*	*Greenhous*

AUSTIN BERKLEY

241. *Swindon Town*

242. *Free transfer*

243. *Mark Dempsey*

244. *Third (behind Dean Spink and Steve Anthrobus on 9%)*

245. *174*

246. *Barnet*

247. *The keyboard*

248. *Robbie Williams*

249. *22*

250. *Gillingham*

PAUL SIMPSON

251. *Five*

252. *Oxford United*

253. *Derby County*

254. *Arsenal*

255. *Rochdale*

256. *Carlisle United*

257. *Billy Davies*

258. *The match-day announcer for a poor selection of music!*

259. *Gary Peters*

260. *2005/2006 as manager of Carlisle United (Rafael Benitez of Liverpool was second)*

WHERE DID THEY GO – 1

261.	*Alan Boswell*	*Wolves*
262.	*Paul Tester*	*Hereford United*
263.	*Derek Price*	*Aldershot*
264.	*Paul Maguire*	*Stoke City*
265.	*David Poutney*	*Aston Villa*
266.	*Carl Leonard*	*Hereford United*

267.	Albert Harley	Swansea
268.	Howard Clark	Hereford United
269.	Ian Atkins	Sunderland
270.	John Arnott	Bournemouth

ARTHUR ROWLEY

271. Record goal scorer
272. 434
273. 1958
274. 1958-1968
275. West Brom
276. 42
277. £7,000
278. Old Division Four
279. Dixie Dean (set in 1939 at Tranmere Rovers, Everton and Notts County)
280. Bradford City

AUTO WINDSCREENS SHIELD RUNNERS-UP - 1996

281. Rotherham United
282. Nigel Jemson
283. Carl Robinson
284. Fred Davies
285. 80th
286. Mark Taylor
287. Bristol Rovers (2-1 on aggregate)
288. Mark Taylor
289. Paul Edwards
290. 18th

NIGEL PEARSON

291. Heanor Town
292. 19 years old
293. Barnsley
294. 1986/87
295. Sheffield Wednesday
296. Middlesbrough
297. Bryan Robson

298. *Carlisle United*

299. *Glenn Roeder*

300. *U21 (caretaker v Italy in 2007 when Stuart Pearce was unavailable)*

WHERE DID THEY COME FROM – 2

301.	*Graeme Worsley*	*Bootle*
302.	*Gary Patterson*	*Notts County*
303.	*Alex McGregor*	*Hibernian*
304.	*Guy Madjo*	*Cheltenham Town*
305.	*Michael Jackson*	*Blackpool*
306.	*Gary Leonard*	*West Bromwich Albion*
307.	*Paul Gorman*	*Carlisle United*
308.	*Kevin McIntyre*	*Macclesfield Town*
309.	*John Arnott*	*West Ham United*
310.	*John Halpin*	*Bury*

2001/2002

311. *Mick Heathcote*

312. *9th*

313. *Hull City*

314. *Nationwide Division Three*

315. *Luke Rodgers*

316. *Ian Woan*

317. *Jamie Tolley*

318. *Plymouth Argyle*

319. *Kevin Ratcliffe*

320. *Nigel Jemson*

IAN ATKINS

321. *1975*

322. *55*

323. *Sunderland*

324. *Alan Brown*

325. *Everton*

326. *GM Vauxhall Conference*

327. *Doncaster Rovers*

328. *Chester City*

329. Torquay United

330. £100,000 (Everton to Ipswich Town in September 1985)

BERNARD McNALLY

331. 1986 (Mexico)

332. Five

333. Shrewsbury

334. Four

335. West Brom

336. £385,000

337. Hednesford Town

338. Telford United

339. The old Second Division

340. India (with Pune FC)

2008/2009

341. Grant Holt

342. Wycombe Wanderers

343. Macclesfield

344. Morecambe

345. Ben Davies (2)

346. Port Vale

347. Chris Humphrey

348. Dagenham & Redbridge

349. Lincoln City

350. Richard Walker (v Lincoln away 0-0)

LEAGUE GOALSCORERS – 2

351.	Mark Atkins	3
352.	Darren Tinson	1
353.	Jake Sedgemore	7
354.	Gavin Cowan	1
355.	Derek Price	28
356.	Glynn Hurst	3
357.	John Manning	18
358.	Carl Griffiths	54
359.	Colin McMenamin	10
360.	Mark Stallard	6

POSITIONS IN THE LEAGUE – 2

361. 1997/1998 13th
362. 1996/1997 22nd
363. 1995/1996 18th
364. 1994/1995 18th
365. 1993/1994 1st
366. 1992/1993 9th
367. 1991/1992 22nd
368. 1990/1991 18th
369. 1989/1990 11th
370. 1988/1989 22nd

DAVID MOYES

371. Juventus
372. Bristol City
373. Nigel Pearson
374. Dunfermline
375. Preston North End
376. Gary Peters
377. Walter Smith
378. Nigel Jemson
379. He scored successive own goals (against Barnsley, West Brom and Colchester)
380. Football agent

2002/2003

381. True
382. Luke Rodgers
383. Nigel Jemson
384. Exeter City
385. Ian Woan
386. True
387. Ryan Lowe
388. Leyton Orient
389. Kevin Ratcliffe
390. Nine

GAY MEADOW

391. 1910
392. Wolves Reserves (Wolves won 2-1)
393. £5,000
394. 10 million
395. Eire
396. Wakeman End
397. 1959
398. Wrestling
399. 1970
400. MK Dons

FOURTH DIVISION RUNNERS-UP – 1974/1975

401. One (they won immediate promotion after relegation in 1974)
402. Alan Durban
403. Mansfield Town
404. 13
405. Doncaster Rovers
406. Ken Mulhearn
407. Ray Haywood (21 league goals)
408. Four (Ken Mulhearn, Jake King, Chic Bates and Ray Haywood)
409. Ian McNeil
410. Brentford

DEBUTS

411. Graham French
412. Graham Turner
413. Colin Robinson
414. Steve Biggins
415. Sir Bobby Charlton
416. Stoke City
417. Tony Kelly
418. Gary Hackett
419. 1973 (March 10)
420. Dave Walton

THE WELSH CUP

421. Six

422. Three

423. It was played on a Sunday, against Christian McNally's beliefs

424. 1988

425. Caernarfon (2-0)

426. Oswestry Town

427. 1891

428. Alf Ellis

429. 1985

430. Wrexham

LEAGUE APPEARANCES – 2

431.	Colin Whitaker	152
432.	Gary Stevens	144 (6)
433.	David Tong	156 (4)
434.	John Moore	144
435.	David Pleat	10 (2)
436.	Jake King	304 (2)
437.	John Hudson	48
438.	Ross MacLaren	158 (3)
439.	Alan Brown	65
440.	Brian Coyne	1

CONFERENCE PLAY-OFF WINNERS – 2003/2004

441. Aldershot

442. 1-1

443. Duane Darby

444. Millennium Stadium, Cardiff

445. Scott Howie

446. 19,216

447. Jimmy Quinn

448. Third

449. Barnet

450. True: won two and drew three

VICTOR KASULE

451. Darlington Town

452. John McGinlay

453. Ian McNeil

454. £35,000

455. All time cult-hero

456. He broke his toe

457. Vodka Vic

458. Singing a George Benson song

459. Uganda

460. Come on as a substitute (for Doug Rougvie) only to be substituted by Dave Geddis without being injured!

HAT-TRICKS

461. Wrexham (he then went 10 games scoreless)

462. Paul Petts

463. Gary Stevens

464. Tony Kelly (against Reading)

465. Billy Richardson

466. 100 goals for Town

467. Frank Clarke

468. Gary Shaw

469. Alf Wood

470. John McGinlay

CHIC BATES

471. Half Man Half Biscuit

472. Three (1984-87, one game in 1999, five games in 2004)

473. Jimmy Quinn

474. Graham Turner (who moved to Aston Villa)

475. Ken Brown (for one week only)

476. Stoke City

477. Lou Macari

478. Chris Kamara

479. Bristol Rovers

480. Tim Yates (he refused to sack his 'friend')

MATCH THE YEAR – 2

481. The club was founded 1886

482. The club won the Third Division title for the first time in their history 1979

483.	*Harry Gregg took over as manager of Shrewsbury Town*	*1968*
484.	*Grant Holt was born*	*1981*
485.	*Michael Jackson joined Town from Blackpool*	*2008*
486.	*The club reached the first ever play-off final at the new Wembley Stadium*	*2007*
487.	*Bournemouth scored against Town after just eight seconds*	*1968*
488.	*Asa Hartford took over as manager of Shrewsbury Town*	*1990*
489.	*Marc Pugh joined Town from Bury*	*2007*
490.	*The club moved to Gay Meadow*	*1910*

DAVID EDWARDS

491. *Pontesbury*

492. *2-1 defeat to Scunthorpe in Shrewsbury's final game before relegation to non-league football*

493. *He had stalled on signing a new contract*

494. *£250,000*

495. *Luton faced financial ruin*

496. *Scunthorpe United*

497. *Wales*

498. *Germany*

499. *Lichtenstein*

500. *19*

JOHN McGINLAY

501. *Ian McNeill*

502. *14 (v Elgin as a substitute)*

503. *Yeovil Town*

504. *Asa Hartford*

505. *£175,000*

506. *The club's greatest ever striker*

507. *Sweden (at Ibrox)*

508. *Bury*

509. *Carl Griffiths*

510. *USA (playing and coaching in Cincinnati)*

THE PROSTAR STADIUM

511. The Gay Meadow stadium
512. July 2007
513. Hall Construction
514. 9,875
515. Amber
516. All-Stars
517. Dave Hibbert
518. Colchester United
519. Darran Kempson
520. True

PETER WILDING

521. Newtown (League of Wales)
522. Paul Edwards (v Torquay United)
523. £10,000
524. Wayne Rooney
525. John Phillips
526. She was in hospital recovering from a knee operation
527. Jimmy Quinn
528. Welshpool Town (League of Wales)
529. Warehouse supervisor for electrical goods factory in Newtown
530. Runs his own plastering business

POSITIONS IN THE LEAGUE - 3

531.	1987/1988	18th
532.	1986/1987	18th
533.	1985/1986	17th
534.	1984/1985	8th
535.	1983/1984	8th
536.	1982/1983	9th
537.	1981/1982	18th
538.	1980/1981	14th
539.	1979/1980	13th
540.	1978/1979	1st

2004/2005

541. 21st

542. Kelvin Langmead and Ciaran Lyng
543. Scunthorpe United
544. Jimmy Quinn, Chic Bates and Gary Peters
545. Chester City
546. False (won one, drew two and lost three)
547. Darren Moss and Luke Rodgers
548. 11
549. Scott Howie
550. Colin Cramb

GREAT ESCAPE – EXETER V SHREWSBURY – MAY 2000

551. 2-1
552. Carlisle United and Chester City
553. Chester City
554. Kevin Ratcliffe
555. John Gayle
556. 84th (Alexander)
557. St James Park
558. Danny Potter
559. Ian Atkins
560. Brighton (2-1)

LEAGUE GOALSCORERS – 3

561.	Eric Brodie	24
562.	Austin Berkley	12
563.	Peter Dolby	21
564.	Roger Preece	3
565.	Paul Maguire	35
566.	David Poutney	11
567.	David Hughes	3
568.	Graham Turner	22
569.	Lee Steele	38
570.	Alf Wood	65

THIRD DIVISION CHAMPIONS – 1993/1994

571. Ray Bailey
572. Preston North End
573. O'Neill Donaldson

574. *Carlisle (1-0)*
575. *Mark Williams*
576. *Mickey Brown*
577. *16*
578. *Dean Spink*
579. *Five*
580. *Chester City*

1970s

581. *Colin Griffin*
582. *John Dungworth (from Aldershot)*
583. *Ran the line after the referee fell sick with 10 minutes remaining*
584. *Alf Wood*
585. *1974/75*
586. *Harry Gregg*
587. *Saudi Arabia*
588. *Five (Harry Gregg, Maurice Evans, Alan Durban, Richie Barker, Graham Turner)*
589. *Brian Hornsby (58 games)*
590. *Five (1-0 win at Watford)*

WAYNE CLARKE

591. *Manchester City (scored six goals in seven games)*
592. *Birmingham City*
593. *Everton (1986/87)*
594. *Old Third Division title*
595. *Ended Liverpool's record breaking run of 30 games unbeaten from start of season*
596: *Walsall*
597. *Five (Frank, Allan, Derek, Kelvin and Wayne)*
598. *Telford United*
599. *Fred Davies*
600. *England youth*

WHERE DID THEY GO – 2

601. *Darran Kempson* *Wrexham*
602. *Derek Asamoah* *Nice*

603.	Sagi Burton	Barnet
604.	Danny Hall	Gretna
605.	Colin Murdock	Accrington
606.	Mark Stallard	Lincoln City
607.	Colin McMenamin	Gretna
608.	Mark Cartwright	Halifax Town
609.	Stephen Jagielka	Sheffield United
610.	Greg Rioch	Northwich Victoria

NIGEL JEMSON

611. Brian Clough
612. Sir Alex Ferguson (Manchester United won and the rest is history!)
613. Sheffield Wednesday
614. Oldham Athletic
615. 58 minutes
616. 15
617. Luke Rodgers (by Thomas Graveson)
618. Ian Woan
619. Bury (Shrews lost 4-3)
620. Ayr United.

KEVIN SUMMERFIELD

621. Youth team coach
622. Paul Sturrock
623. Plymouth Argyle
624. 168
625. Six
626. 1990/91
627. Plymouth Argyle
628. Cardiff City
629. Southampton
630. Free transfer

2007/2008

631. Lincoln City
632. Andy Cooke
633. Stockport County

634. Paul Simpson
635. 18th
636. Dave Hibbert
637. Asa Hall and Guy Madjo
638. Six
639. Michael Symes
640. False: won one, drew two and lost two

CARL GRIFFITHS

641. Manchester City
642. Leeds United
643. Million-pound teenager
644. Ian McNeil
645. Manchester City
646. Paul Walsh
647. Braintree Town (he missed the match with a calf injury)
648. Manchester City
649. Gary Peters
650. Luton Town

THIRD DIVISION CHAMPIONS – 1978/1979

651. Richie Barker (until November 1978)
652. Graham Turner
653. Exeter City
654. 4-1
655. Manchester City (2-0)
656. 10
657. Watford
658. Colin Griffin
659. Jake King
660. Paul Maguire

WHO AM I? – 2

661. Dave Hibbert
662. Mickey Brown
663. Andy Cooke
664. Kelvin Langmead
665. Tim Steele

666. Mickey Brown
667. Mark Williams
668. Spencer Whelan
669. Graham Coughlan
670. Marc Tierney

HONOURS

671.	League Cup semi-finalists	1961
672.	Third Division Champions	1979
673.	Fourth Division runners-up	1975
674.	Conference play-off winners	2004
675.	League Two finalists	2007
676.	Welsh Cup winners	1985
677.	Football League Trophy runners-up	1996
678.	Welsh Cup winners	1980
679.	Football League Trophy area finalists	2003
680.	Third Division Champions	1994

MICKEY BROWN

681. 418
682. Three
683. Bolton Wanderers
684. Preston North End
685. 58 minutes
686. Steve Jagielka
687. Boston United
688. Newtown
689. Modelling men's underwear: www.deadgoodundies.com
690. A knighthood ('Sir' Mickey Brown)

2005/2006

691. Gary Peters
692. Colin McMenamin
693. Kelvin Langmead
694. Six
695. Leyton Orient
696. 10th
697. Mark Stallard

698. *Rochdale*

699. *Wrexham*

700. *Kelvin Langmead*

POT LUCK - 1

701. *Alcohol licence (even for the director's box!)*

702. *English Cricket Cup (beating Hastings and St Leonards at Lord's with fast bowler 'Oggie' in form)*

703. *Closed circuit TV cameras*

704. *Nottingham Forest*

705. *Malcolm Starkey*

706. *Birmingham (won 2-1)*

707. *Alan Parry*

708. *Eight seconds (Keith East for Bournemouth)*

709. *Paul Petts*

710. *Tim Yates (former chairman)*

LEAGUE APPEARANCES – 3

711.	*John Parr*	*112*
712.	*David Linighan*	*65*
713.	*John McGinlay*	*58 (2)*
714.	*Wayne Clarke*	*34 (1)*
715.	*David Geddis*	*36 (3)*
716.	*Carl Griffiths*	*110 (34)*
717.	*Steve Ogrizovic*	*84*
718.	*Graham Turner*	*342 (13)*
719.	*Darren Hughes*	*34 (3)*
720.	*Alan Groves*	*76*

POT LUCK - 2

721. *Geoffrey Boycott (for 27 runs)*

722. *Clay Pigeon shooting*

723. *The League had not been informed that the first Saturday clashed with the Shrewsbury Flower Show*

724. *Mark Taylor*

725. *The Coracle Man (retrieving the balls from the River Severn)*

726. *The Welsh FA selected to play it in Shrewsbury as a 'home' venue*

727. *This is Spinal Tap*

728. Mark Williams

729. Dave Clark Five

730. 40 (if you exclude the 2-0 win over Wolves St Georges who later withdrew from the league with all results expunged)

GARY PETERS

731. David Moyes (at Everton)

732. Reading

733. Fulham

734. Preston North End

735. November 2004

736. Jimmy Quinn

737. 10th

738. Six

739. Barnet

740. David Beckham

WHERE DID THEY COME FROM – 3

741.	Ben Davies	Chester City
742.	Sagi Burton	Peterborough United
743.	Kevin Street	Bristol Rovers
744.	Trevor Challis	Telford
745.	Ian Dunbavin	Liverpool
746.	Spencer Whelan	Chester City
747.	Darren Currie	West Ham United
748.	Darren Rowbotham	Crewe Alexandra
749.	Ian Stevens	Bury
750.	Mark Taylor	Sheffield Wednesday

1960s

751. Polio

752. Bingo

753. Czechoslovakia

754. Millwall (won 2-1)

755. Bournemouth (he scored the Town goal)

756. First Town player to come on as a substitute since the new law was introduced

757. David Pleat

758. Bury

759. Harry Gregg

760. Dave Poutney

SQUAD NUMBERS – 2008/2009 – 2

761.	David Hunt	6
762.	Michael Jackson	4
763.	Glyn Garner	1
764.	Jasbir Singh	22
765.	David Maguire	30
766.	Marc Tierney	23
767.	Grant Holt	16
768.	Paul Murray	15
769.	Shane Cansdell-Sherriff	24
770.	Chris Humphrey	17

WHERE DID THEY GO – 3

771.	Austin Berkley	Barnet
772.	Roger Preece	Telford
773.	Devon White	Ilkeston Town
774.	Darren Rowbotham	Exeter City
775.	Steve Anthrobus	Crewe Alexandra
776.	Mark Williams	Chesterfield Town
777.	O'Neill Donaldson	Doncaster Rovers
778.	Mark Blake	Fulham
779.	Gary Patterson	Wycombe Wanderers
780.	Howard Clark	Hereford United

BIG WINS – 2

781.	v. Aldershot (home), 2 February 1952, League	5-1
782.	v. Watford (home), August 1953, League	6-4
783.	v. Swindon Town (home), May 1955, League	7-0
784.	v. Norwich City (home), August 1955, League	6-0

785. v. Swindon Town (home), December 1956, League 7-3

786. v. Southport (home), December 1958, League 6-2

787. v. Accrington Stanley (home), August 1959, League 5-0

788. v. Chelmsford City (away), November 1962, FA Cup 1st round 6-2

789. v. Luton Town (away), March 1965, League 7-2

790. v. Scunthorpe United (home), April 1968, League 4-0

LEAGUE TWO PLAY-OFF FINALISTS – 2006/2007

791. Bristol Rovers

792. Stuart Drummond

793. Marc Tierney

794. Wembley

795. 61,589

796. 7th

797. 18

798. Gary Peters

799. Boston United

800. False: won three, drew three and lost one

NOTES

NOTES

NOTES

NOTES

NOTES

NOTES

NOTES

NOTES